Who Likes the Cold?

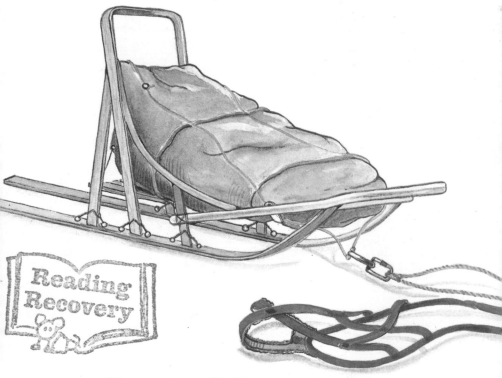

Reading Recovery

Story by Rebel Williams

Illustrations by Iris Nichols

Polar bears like the cold.

2

Puffins like the cold.

Penguins like the cold.

Walruses like the cold.

Foxes like the cold.

Reindeer like the cold.

And so do I!